This edition copyright © Robert Frederick Ltd.
Downwood, Claverton Down Road, Bath BA2 6DT
First Published 1993
All rights reserved.

Acknowledgments
Typesetting by Creative Design & Typesetting;
Printed in the UK

The Sherlock Holmes
Journal

"He is a little queer in his ideas – an enthusiast in some branches of science. As far as I know he is a decent fellow enough. . . . I believe he is well up in anatomy, and he is a first-class chemist; but, as far as I know, he has never taken out any systematic medical classes. His studies are desultory and eccentric, but he has amassed a lot of out-of-the-way knowledge which would astonish his professors." [Stamford]

A Study in Scarlet

Holmes was accessible upon the side of flattery, and also, to do him justice, upon the side of kindliness.

The Red Circle

"Beyond the obvious facts that he has at some time done manual labour, that he takes snuff, that he is a Freemason, that he has been in China, and that he has done a considerable amount of writing lately, I can deduce nothing else."

The Red-headed League

"The pipe was still between his lips."

"To a great mind,
nothing is little."

A Study in Scarlet

Sherlock Holmes was a man who seldom took exercise for exercise's sake. Few men were capable of greater muscular effort, and he was undoubtedly one of the finest boxers of his weight that I have ever seen, but he looked upon aimless bodily exertion as a waste of energy, and he seldom bestirred himself save where there was some professional object to be served. That he should have kept himself in training under such circumstances is remarkable, but his diet was usually of the sparest, and his habits were simple to the verge of austerity. Save for the occasional use of cocaine he had no vices, and he only turned to the drug as a protest against the monotony of existence when cases were scanty and the papers uninteresting.

The Yellow Face

The Sherlock Holmes Journal

Important Events

The Sherlock Holmes Journal

Holmes: "I clambered over the fence into the grounds."

Phelps: "Surely the gate was open?"

Holmes: "Yes, but I have a peculiar taste in these matters."

The Naval Treaty

"And the murderer?"
"Is a tall man, left-handed, limps with the right leg, wears thick-soled shooting boots and a grey cloak, smokes Indian cigars, uses a cigar-holder, and carries a blunt penknife in his pocket.   There are several other indications, but these may be enough to aid us in our search."

The Boscombe Valley Mystery

I have seldom known him claim any large reward for his inestimable services. So unworldly was he – or so capricious – that he frequently refused his help to the powerful and wealthy where the problem made no appeal to his sympathies.

Black Peter

The Sherlock Holmes Journal

Important Events

Sherlock Holmes was transformed when he was hot upon such a scent as this. Men who had only known the quiet thinker and logician of Baker Street would have failed to recognize him.

The Boscombe Valley Mystery

He had, when he so willed it, the utter immobility of countenance of a Red Indian.

The Naval Treaty

To his sombre and cynical spirit all popular applause was always abhorrent, and nothing amused him more at the end of a successful case than to hand over the actual exposure to some orthodox official.

The Devil's Foot

The clear, hard eyes were dimmed for a moment, and the firm lips were shaking. For the one and only time I caught a glimpse of a great heart as well as of a great brain.

The Three Garridebs

"Then he stood before the fire."

I descended to breakfast prepared to find my companion in depressed spirits, for, like all great artists, he was easily impressed by his surroundings.

Thor Bridge

"I made a blunder, my dear Watson – which is, I am afraid, a more common occurrence than anyone would think who only know me through your memoirs.

The Silver Blaze

"Never trust to general impressions, my boy, but concentrate yourself upon details. My first glance is always at a woman's sleeve. In a man it is perhaps better first to take the knee of the trouser."

A Case of Identity

Sherlock Holmes was pacing up and down the platform, his tall, gaunt figure made even gaunter and taller by his long grey travelling cloak, and close-fitting cloth cap.

The Boscombe Valley Mystery

The Sherlock Holmes Journal

Important Events

_____

_____

_____

_____

_____

_____

_____

_____

_____

_____

_____

_____

_____

_____

_____

_____

_____

_____

_____

_____

_____

_____

_____

_____

Problems may be solved in the study which have baffled all those who have sought a solution by the aid of their senses.

The Five Orange Pips

"I choose to be only associated with those crimes which present some difficulty in their solution."

The Cardboard Box

"You will remember, Watson, how the dreadful business of the Abernetty family was first brought to my notice by the depth which the parsley had sunk into the butter on a hot day."

The Six Napoleons

"As you are aware, Watson, there is no one who knows the higher criminal world of London so well as I do."

The Final Problem

"It has long been an axiom of mine that the little things are infinitely the most important."

A Case of Identity

The Sherlock Holmes Journal

Important Events

_____

_____

_____

_____

_____

_____

_____

_____

_____

_____

_____

"I have seen too much not to know that the impression of a woman may be more valuable than the conclusion of an analytical reasoner."

The Man with the Twisted Lip

"It is quite a three-pipe problem, and I beg that you won't speak to me for fifty minutes."

The Red-headed League

"The principal difficulty in your case," remarked Holmes, in his didactic fashion, "lay in the fact of there being too much evidence. What was vital was overlaid and hidden by what was irrelevant."

The Naval Treaty

"Why," said I, glancing up at my companion, "that was surely the bell. Who could come to-night? Some friend of yours, perhaps?"
"Except yourself I have none," he answered. "I do not encourage visitors."

The Five Orange Pips

"We strolled about together."

There was something in his masterly grasp of a situation, and his keen, incisive reasoning, which made it a pleasure to me to study his system of work, and to follow the quick, subtle methods by which he disentangled the most inextricable mysteries. So accustomed was I to his invariable success that the very possibility of his failing had ceased to enter into my head.

A Scandal in Bohemia

"It is my business to know things. Perhaps I have trained myself to see what others overlook."

A Case of Identity

"I think we'll shut that window again, if you don't mind. It is a singular thing, but I find that a concentrated atmosphere helps a concentration of thought. I have not pushed it to the length of getting into a box to think, but that is the logical outcome of my convictions."

The Hound of the Baskervilles

He was, I take it, the most perfect reasoning and observing machine that the world has seen; but, as a lover, he would have placed himself in a false position.

A Scandal in Bohemia

"I think that I may go so far as to say, Watson, that I have not lived wholly in vain. If my record were closed tonight I could still survey it with equanimity. The air of London is the sweeter for my presence. In over a thousand cases I am not aware that I have ever used my powers upon the wrong side. Of late I have been tempted to look into the problems furnished by Nature rather than those more superficial ones for which our artificial state of society is responsible."

The Final Problem

"I am inclined to think —"
said I.
"I should think so."
Sherlock Holmes remarked,
impatiently.

The Valley of Fear

"You can . . . never foretell what any one man will do, but you can say with precision what an average number will be up to. Individuals vary, but percentages remain constant."

The Sign of Four

"When you follow two separate chains of thought, Watson, you will find some point of intersection which should approximate to the truth."

The Disappearance of Lady Frances Carfax

His [Sherlock Holmes'] aversion to women, and his disinclination to form new friendships, were both typical of his unemotional character, but not more so than his complete suppression of every reference to his own people. I had come to believe that he was an orphan with no relatives living, but one day, to my very great surprise, he began to talk to me about his brother.

The Greek Interpreter

" 'Come, Watson, come!' he cried. 'The game is afoot.' "

Sherlock Holmes had, in a very remarkable degree, the power of detaching his mind at will. For two hours the strange business in which we had been involved appeared to be forgotten, and he was entirely absorbed in the pictures of the modern Belgian master.

The Hound of the Baskervilles

"There's the scarlet thread of murder running through the colourless skein of life, and our duty is to unravel it, and isolate it, and expose every inch of it."

A Study in Scarlet

"I found the ash of a cigar, which my special knowledge of tobacco ashes enabled me to pronounce as an Indian cigar. I have, as you know, devoted some attention to this, and written a little monograph on the ashes of 140 different varieties of pipe, cigar, and cigarette tobacco."

The Boscombe Valley Mystery

The Sherlock Holmes Journal

Important Events

_____

_____

_____

_____

_____

_____

_____

_____

_____

_____

_____

_____

_____

_____

_____

_____

_____

_____

_____

_____

_____

_____

_____

"I am afraid that I rather give myself away when I explain." said he. "Results without causes are much more impressive."

The Stockbroker's Clerk

"You have a grand gift of silence, Watson." said he. "It makes you quite invaluable as a companion. 'Pon my word, it is a great thing for me to have someone to talk to, for my own thoughts are not over pleasant."

The Man with the Twisted Lip

I had already observed that he was as sensitive to flattery on the score of his art as any girl could be of her beauty.

A Study in Scarlet

"So, my dear Watson, there's my report of a failure. And yet – and yet –" – he clenched his thin hands in a paroxysm of conviction – "I know it's all wrong. I feel it in my bones."

The Norwood Builder

The Sherlock Holmes Journal

Important Events

"You really are an automaton – a calculating machine . . . there is really something positively inhuman in you at times." "It is of the first importance not to allow your judgment to be biased by personal qualities."

The Sign of Four

He was thin and worn, but clear and alert, his keen face bronzed by the sun and roughened by the wind. In his tweed suit and cloth cap he looked like any other tourist upon the moor, and he had contrived, with that cat-like love of personal cleanliness which was one of his characteristics, that his chin should be as smooth and his linen as perfect as if he were in Baker Street.

The Hound of the Baskervilles

"Quite so." he answered, throwing himself down into an armchair. "You see, but you do not observe. The distinction is clear."

A Scandal in Bohemia

"The driver pointed with his whip — 'Baskerville Hall', said he."

"In a modest way I have combated evil, but to take on the Father of Evil himself would, perhaps, be too ambitious a task."

The Hound of the Baskervilles

Bradstreet: "I wish I knew how you reach your results."
Holmes: "I reached this one by sitting upon five pillows and consuming an ounce of shag."

The Man with the Twisted Lip

In glancing over my notes of the seventy odd cases in which I have during the last eight years studied the methods of my friend Sherlock Holmes, I find many tragic, some comic, a large number merely strange, but none commonplace; for, working as he did rather for the love of his art than for the acquirement of wealth, he refused to associate himself with any investigation which did not tend towards the unusual, and even the fantastic.

The Speckled Band

The Sherlock Holmes Journal

Important Events

_____

_____

_____

_____

_____

_____

_____

_____

_____

_____

_____

_____

_____

_____

_____

_____

_____

_____

_____

_____

_____

_____

_____

The Sherlock Holmes Journal

"Ha, you see it now. My eyes have been trained to examine faces and not their trimmings. It is the first quality of a criminal investigator that he should see through a disguise."

The Hound of the Baskervilles

"The larger crimes are apt to be the simpler, for the bigger the crime, the more obvious, as a rule, is the motive."

A Case of Identity

"It is an old maxim of mine that when you have excluded the impossible, whatever remains, however improbable, must be the truth."

The Beryl Coronet

"Once or twice in my career I feel that I have done more real harm by my discovery of the criminal than ever he had done by his crime. I have learned caution now, and I had rather play tricks with the law of England than with my own conscience."

The Abbey Grange

The Sherlock Holmes Journal

Important Events

_____
_____
_____
_____
_____
_____
_____
_____
_____
_____
_____
_____
_____
_____
_____
_____
_____
_____
_____
_____
_____
_____
_____
_____
_____

The Sherlock Holmes Journal

"I am the last and highest court of appeal in detection."

The Sign of Four

Sherlock Holmes was transformed when he was hot upon such a scent as this. Men who had only known the quiet thinker and logician of Baker Street would have failed to recognise him. His face flushed and darkened. His brows were drawn into two hard, black lines, while his eyes shone out from beneath them with a steely glitter. His face was bent downwards, his shoulders bowed, his lips compressed, and the veins stood out like whipcord in his long, sinewy neck. His nostrils seemed to dilate with a purely animal lust for the chase, and his mind was so absolutely concentrated upon the matter before him, that a question or remark fell unheeded upon his ears, or at the most, only provoked a quick, impatient snarl in reply.

The Boscombe Valley Mystery

"Holmes gazed at it, and then passed on."

"Pipes are occasionally of extraordinary interest." said he. "Nothing has more individuality save, perhaps, watches and bootlaces."

The Yellow Face

"Holmes is a little too scientific for my tastes – it approaches to cold-bloodedness. I could imagine his giving a friend a little pinch of the latest vegetable alkaloid, not out of malevolence, you understand, but simply out of a spirit of inquiry in order to have an accurate idea of the effects. To do him justice, I think that he would take it himself with the same readiness."

[Stamford]

A Study in Scarlet

He held out his snuffbox of old gold, with a great amethyst in the centre of the lid. Its splendour was in such contrast to his homely ways and simple life that I could not help commenting upon it.

A Case of Identity

The Sherlock Holmes Journal

Important Events

_____

_____

_____

_____

_____

_____

_____

_____

_____

_____

_____

_____

_____

_____

_____

_____

_____

_____

_____

_____

_____

_____

_____

_____

"The ideal reasoner," he remarked, "would, when he has once been shown a single fact in all its bearings, deduce from it not only all the chain of events which led up to it, but also all the results which would follow from it."

The Five Orange Pips

He was bright, eager, and in excellent spirits, a mood which in his case alternated with fits of the blackest depression.

The Sign of Four

It was difficult to refuse any of Sherlock Holmes' requests, for they were always so exceedingly defi-nite, and put forward with such an air of mastery.

The Man with the Twisted Lip

"As a rule, when I have heard some slight indication of the course of events I am able to guide myself by the thousands of other similar cases which occur to my memory."

The Red-headed League

The Sherlock Holmes Journal

Important Events

_____

_____

_____

_____

_____

_____

_____

_____

_____

_____

_____

_____

_____

_____

_____

_____

_____

_____

_____

_____

_____

_____

_____

_____

"I know, my dear Watson, that you share my love of all that is bizarre and outside the conventions and humdrum routine of everyday life. You have shown your relish for it by the enthusiasm which has prompted you to chronicle, and, if you will excuse my saying so, somewhat embellish so many of my own little adventures."

The Red-headed League

Both Holmes and I had a weakness for the Turkish Bath. It was over a smoke in the pleasant lassitude of the drying room that I have found him less reticent and more human than anywhere else.

The Illustrious Client

Appreciation of Nature found no place among his many gifts, and his only change was when he turned his mind from the evil-doer of the town to track down his brother of the country.

The Cardboard Box

"He turned over the pages lazily, leaning back in his chair."

"Not Mr. Sherlock Holmes!" roared the prize-fighter. "God's truth! how could I have mistook you? If instead o' standin' there so quiet you had just stepped up and given me that cross-hit of yours under the jaw, I'd ha' known you without a question. Ah, you're the one that has wasted your gifts, you have! You might have aimed high, if you had joined the fancy."

The Sign of Four

"You may place considerable confidence in Mr. Holmes, sir." said the police agent, loftily. "He has his own little methods, which are, if he won't mind my saying so, just a little too theoretical and fantastic, but he has the makings of a detective in him. It is not too much to say that once or twice, as in that business of the Sholto murder and the Agra treasure, he has been more nearly correct than the official force."

The Red-headed League

The Sherlock Holmes Journal

Important Events

_____

_____

_____

_____

_____

_____

_____

_____

_____

_____

_____

_____

_____

_____

_____

_____

_____

_____

_____

_____

_____

_____

_____

_____

_____

His cold and proud nature was always averse, however, to anything in the shape of public applause, and he bound me in the most stringent terms to say no further word of himself, his methods, or his successes – a prohibition which, as I have explained, has only now been removed.

The Norwood Builder

Holmes: "I followed you."
Sterndale: "I saw no one."
Holmes: "That is what you may expect to see when I follow you."

The Devil's Foot

He burst into one of his rare fits of laughter as he turned away from the picture. I have not heard him laugh often, and it has always boded ill to somebody.

The Hound of the Baskervilles

"There's no branch of detective science which is so important and so much neglected as the art of tracing footsteps."

A Study in Scarlet

The Sherlock Holmes Journal

Important Events

_____

_____

_____

_____

_____

_____

_____

_____

_____

_____

_____

_____

_____

_____

_____

_____

_____

_____

_____

_____

"I assure you that the most winning woman I ever knew was hanged for poisoning three little children for their insurance-money."

The Sign of Four

"As a rule," said Holmes, "the more bizarre a thing is the less mysterious it proves to be. It is your commonplace, featureless crimes which are really puzzling, just as a commonplace face is the most difficult to identify.

The Red-headed League

"I assure you Watson, without affectation, that the status of my client is a matter of less moment to me than the interest of his case."

The Noble Bachelor

"You speak of danger. You have evidently seen more in these rooms than was visible to me."
"No, but I fancy that I may have deduced a little more. I imagine that you saw all that I did."

The Speckled Band

"There stood a patriarch among oaks."

During my long and inti-
mate acquaintance with
Mr. Sherlock Holmes I had
never heard him refer to his
relations, and hardly ever to
his own early life. This reti-
cence upon his part had
increased the somewhat
inhuman effect which he
produced upon me, until
sometimes I found myself
regarding him as an isolated
phenomenon, a brain with-
out a heart, as deficient in
human sympathy as he was
pre-eminent in intelligence.

The Greek Interpreter

All the afternoon he sat in
the stalls wrapped in the
most perfect happiness,
gently waving his long thin
fingers in time to the music,
while his gently smiling
face and his languid,
dreamy eyes were as unlike
those of Holmes the sleuth-
hound, Holmes the
relentless, keen-witted,
ready-handed criminal
agent, as it was possible to
conceive. In his singular
character the dual nature
alternately asserted itself.

The Red-headed League

He took up his violin from the corner, and as I stretched myself out he began to play some low, dreamy, melodious air – his own, no doubt, for he had a remarkable gift for improvisation. I have a vague remembrance of his gaunt limbs, his earnest face, and the rise and fall of his bow.

The Sign of Four

When we rose again I observed that Holmes's eyes were shining and his cheeks tinged with colour. Only at a crisis have I seen those battle-signals flying.

The Gold Pince-Nez

"Circumstantial evidence is a very tricky thing," answered Holmes thoughtfully; "it may seem to point very straight to one thing, but if you shift your own point of view a little, you may find it pointing in an equally uncompromising manner to something entirely different."

The Boscombe Valley Mystery

The Sherlock Holmes Journal

Important Events

_____

_____

_____

_____

_____

_____

_____

_____

_____

_____

_____

_____

_____

_____

_____

_____

_____

_____

_____

_____

_____

_____

"For example, how did you deduce that this man was intellectual?" For answer Holmes clapped the hat upon his head. It came right over the forehead and settled upon the bridge of his nose. "It is a question of cubic capacity," said he; "a man with so large a brain must have something in it."

The Blue Carbuncle

One of Sherlock Holmes's defects – if, indeed, one may call it a defect – was that he was exceedingly loth to communicate his full plans to any other person until the instant of their fulfilment.

The Hound of the Baskervilles

He would devote weeks of most intense application to the affairs of some humble client whose case presented those strange and dramatic qualities which appealed to his imagination and challenged his ingenuity.

Black Peter

"His eyes bent upon the glow of the fire."

"Ah, you rogue!" cried Jones, highly delighted. "You would have made an actor, and a rare one. You had the proper workhouse cough, and those weak legs of yours are worth ten pounds a week."

The Sign of Four

A flush of colour sprang to Holmes's pale cheeks, and he bowed to us like the master dramatist who receives the homage of his audience. ... The same singularly proud and reserved nature which turned away with disdain from popular notoriety was capable of being moved to its depths by spontaneous wonder and praise from a friend.

The Six Napoleons

My friend's temper had not improved since he had been deprived of the congenial surroundings of Baker Street. Without his scrapbooks, his chemicals, and his homely untidiness, he was an uncomfortable man.

The Three Students

The swing of his nature took him from extreme languor to devouring energy; and, as I knew well, he was never so truly formidable as when, for days on end, he had been lounging in his arm-chair amid his improvisations and his black-letter editions. Then it was that the lust of the chase would suddenly come upon him, and that his brilliant reasoning power would rise to the level of intuition, until those who were unacquainted with his methods would look askance at him as on a man whose knowledge was not that of other mortals.

The Red-headed League

So long as he was in actual professional practice the records of his successes were of some practical value to him; but since he has definitely retired from London and betaken himself to study and bee-farming on the Sussex Downs, notoriety has become hateful to him.

The Second Stain

The Sherlock Holmes Journal

Important Events

I had no keener pleasure than in following Holmes in his professional investigations, and in admiring the rapid deductions, as swift as intuitions, and yet always founded on a logical basis, with which he unravelled the problems which were submitted to him.

The Speckled Band

"You know my method. It is founded upon the observance of trifles."

The Boscombe Valley Mystery

"Do you know, Watson," said he, "that it is one of the curses of a mind with a turn like mine that I must look at everything with reference to my own special subject. You look at these scattered houses, and you are impressed by their beauty. I look at them, and the only thought which comes to me is a feeling of their isolation, and of the impunity with which crime may be committed there."

The Copper Beeches

"Holmes was working hard over a chemical investigation."

"If there's a vacant place for a chief of the police, I reckon you are the man for it."

(Jefferson Hope to Holmes]

A Study in Scarlet

"There is nothing more deceptive than an obvious fact."

The Boscombe Valley Mystery

"Thank you!" said Holmes. "Thank you!" and as he turned away it seemed to me that he was more nearly moved by the softer human emotions than I had ever seen him. A moment later he was the cold and practical thinker once more.

The Six Napoleons

Holmes grinned . . . "Well," he said, "I say now, as I said then, that a man should keep his little brain attic stocked with all the furniture that he is likely to use, and the rest he can put away in the lumber room of his library, where he can get it if he wants it."

The Five Orange Pips

The Sherlock Holmes Journal

Important Events

_____

_____

_____

_____

_____

_____

_____

_____

_____

_____

_____

_____

_____

_____

_____

_____

_____

_____

_____

_____

_____

The Sherlock Holmes Journal

Openshaw: "He said that you could solve anything."

Holmes: "He said too much."

Openshaw: "That you are never beaten."

Holmes: "I have been beaten four times – three times by men, and once by a woman."

The Five Orange Pips

Accustomed as I was to my friend's amazing powers in the use of disguises, I had to look three times before I was certain it was indeed he.

A Scandal in Bohemia

"It saved me from ennui." he answered, yawning. "Alas! I already feel it closing in upon me. My life is spent in one long effort to escape from the commonplaces of existence. These little problems help me to do so."

The Red-headed League

It was when he was at his wits' end that his energy and his versatility were most admirable.

The Yellow Face

The Sherlock Holmes Journal

Important Events

_____

_____

_____

_____

_____

_____

_____

_____

_____

_____

_____

_____

_____

_____

_____

_____

_____

_____

_____

_____

_____

_____

_____

_____

As to my companion, neither the country nor the sea presented the slightest attraction to him. He loved to lie in the very centre of five millions of people, with his filaments stretching out and running through them, responsive to every little rumour or suspicion of unsolved crime.

The Cardboard Box

" 'Pon my word, Watson, you are coming along wonderfully. You have really done very well indeed. It is true that you have missed everything of importance, but you have hit upon the method, and you have a quick eye for colour."

A Case of Identity

"Elementary. It is one of those instances when the reasoner can produce an effect which seems remarkable to his neighbour, because the latter has missed the one little point which is the basis of the deduction."

The Crooked Man

"There's our man Watson! Come along."

Holmes was cold and stern and silent. As the gleam of the street-lamps flashed upon his austere features I saw that his brows were drawn down in thought and his thin lips compressed. I knew not what wild beast we were about to hunt down in the dark jungle of criminal London, but I was well assured from the bearing of this master huntsman that the adventure was a most grave one, while the sardonic smile which occasionally broke through his ascetic gloom boded little good for the object of our quest.

The Empty House

"The days of the great cases are past. Man, or at last criminal man, has lost all enterprise and originality. As to my own little practice, it seems to be degenerating into an agency for recovering lost lead pencils, and giving advice to young ladies from boarding school. I think that I have touched bottom at last."

The Copper Beeches

_____
_____
_____
_____
_____
_____
_____
_____
_____
_____
_____
_____
_____
_____
_____
_____
_____
_____
_____
_____
_____

The Sherlock Holmes Journal

Important Events

An anomaly which often struck me in the character of my friend Sherlock Holmes was that, although in his methods of thought he was the neatest and most methodical of mankind, and although also he affected a certain quiet primness of dress, he was none the less in his personal habits one of the most untidy men that ever drove a fellow-lodger to distraction.

The Musgrave Ritual

He had an almost hypnotic power of soothing when he wished.

The Red Circle

"Not invisible, but unnoticed, Watson. You did not know where to look, and so you missed all that was important. I can never bring you to realise the importance of sleeves, the suggestiveness of thumbnails, or the great issues that may hang from a bootlace."

A Case of Identity

The Sherlock Holmes Journal

Important Events

_____

_____

_____

_____

_____

_____

_____

_____

_____

_____

_____

_____

_____

_____

_____

_____

_____

_____

_____

_____

See the foxhound with hanging ears and drooping tail . . . and compare it with the same hound as, with gleaming eyes and straining muscles, it runs upon a breast-high scent – such was the change in Holmes since the morning.

The Bruce-Partington Plans

It was not merely that Holmes changed his costume. His expression, his manner, his very soul seemed to vary with every fresh part that he assumed. The stage lost a fine actor, even as science lost an acute reasoner, when he became a specialist in crime.

A Scandal in Bohemia

"I cannot agree with those who rank modesty among the virtues. To a logician all things should be seen exactly as they are, and to underestimate oneself is as much a departure from the truth as to exaggerate one's powers."

The Greek Interpreter

The death of Sherlock Holmes.

"Depend upon it, there is nothing so unnatural as the commonplace."

A Case of Identity

"I read nothing except the criminal news and the agony column. The latter is always instructive."

The Noble Bachelor

"If I claim full justice for my art, it is because it is an impersonal thing – a thing beyond myself. Crime is common. Logic is rare. Therefore it is upon the logic rather than upon the crime that you should dwell."

The Copper Beeches

Sherlock Holmes was a past master in the art of putting a humble witness at his ease.

The Missing Three-quarter

The strong, masterful personality of Holmes dominated the tragic scene, and all were equally puppets in his hands.

The Solitary Cyclist

The Sherlock Holmes Journal

Important Events

One of the most remarkable characteristics of Sherlock Holmes was his power of throwing his brain out of action and switching all his thoughts on to lighter things whenever he had convinced himself that he could no longer work to advantage.

The Bruce-Partington Plans

Something in his tone caught my ear, and I turned to look at him. An extraordinary change had come over his face. It was writhing with inward merriment. His two eyes were shining like stars. It seemed to me that he was making desperate efforts to restrain a convulsive attack of laughter.

The Norwood Builder

"My dear fellow," said Sherlock Holmes, as we sat on either side of the fire in his lodgings at Baker Street, "life is infinitely stranger than anything which the mind of man could invent."

A Case of Identity

The Sherlock Holmes Journal

Important Events

_____

_____

_____

_____

_____

_____

_____

_____

_____

_____

_____

_____

_____

_____

_____

_____

_____

_____

_____

_____

_____

_____

_____

_____

_____